Scholastic's The Magic School Bus

Adventures in the Food Chain
Coloring and Activity Book

Written by Pat Relf
Illustrated by Steve Haefele

Based on the animated TV series
produced by Scholastic Productions, Inc.
Based on *The Magic School Bus* books
written by Joanna Cole and illustrated by Bruce Degen

TV tie-in book by Patricia Relf and illustrated by Steve Haefele.
Cover illustration by Nancy Stevenson.

ISBN 0-590-60408-2

12 11 10 9 8 7 6 5 4 3 2   2 3 4 5/0

Printed in the U.S.A.   40
First Scholastic printing, September 1995

SCHOLASTIC INC.
New York   Toronto   London   Auckland   Sydney

A New Leaf

Our teacher is Ms. Frizzle. She's the strangest teacher in the school.

Today we are learning about food chains. Every class learns about food chains. But not every teacher teaches like Ms. Frizzle.

Color this picture any way you'd like!

Tossed Salad

Every living thing needs energy. Animals get energy from eating plants and other animals. Where do plants get their energy? To find out, try this puzzle. Each mixed-up word is the name of a plant that people or animals eat. Unscramble the words. Then write the circled letters on the lines below.

— — — — — — — —

MATOOT — — — — ◯ —

YAH ◯ — —

ERIC — — — ◯

SAGRS — — ◯ — — —

CUTLEET — — — — ◯ — —

NROC — — ◯ — .

Answers on page 31.

Eat Your Veggies

Some animals eat *only* plants. They are called herbivores.
Draw lines to match the herbivore with its food.

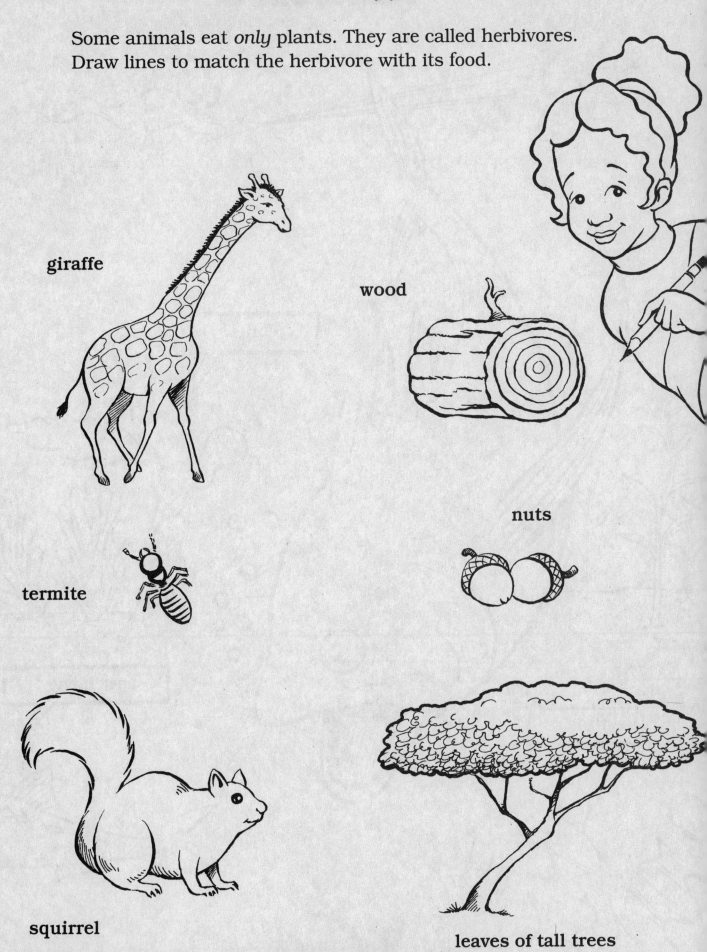

giraffe

wood

nuts

termite

squirrel

leaves of tall trees

Answers on page 31.

Seafood Diet

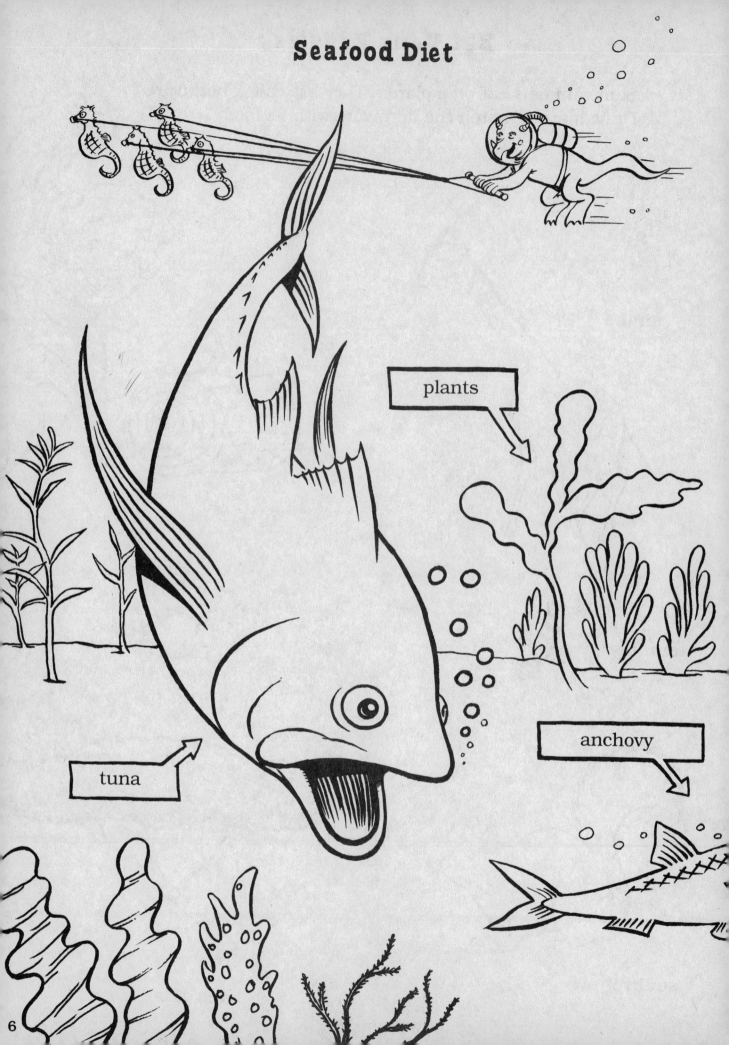

Our class is on a field trip ... in the deep ocean.
We seem to have shrunk to the size of a tuna.
That anchovy is eating those copepods!
And the tuna is about to eat the anchovy.
Color this picture any way you'd like.

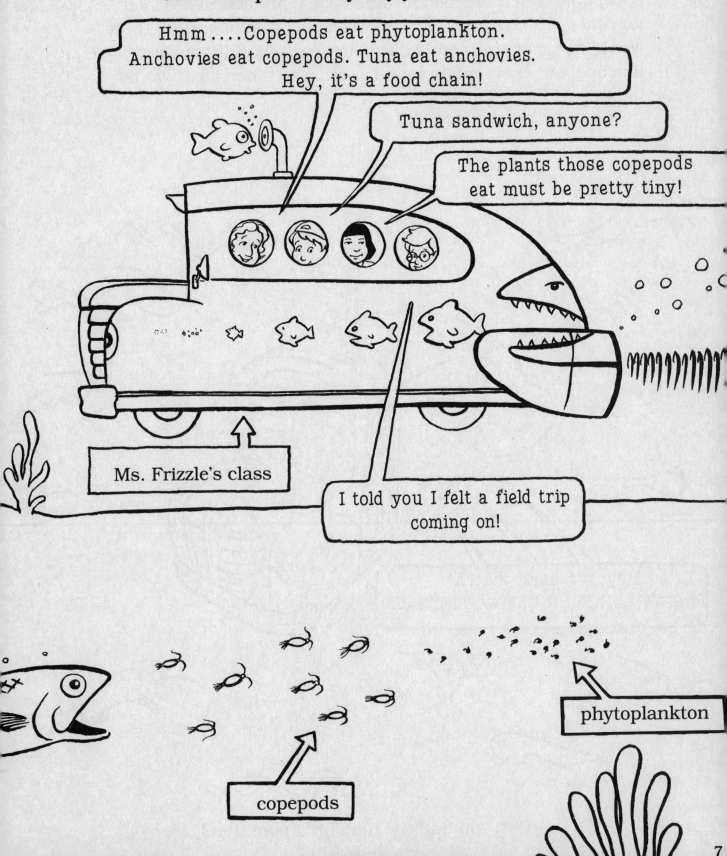

Tiny Twins

Wow! Now our bus is so tiny you would need a microscope to see it! Look at all these phytoplankton. These tiny creatures use the energy of the sun to grow. Phytoplankton are food for copepods, which are food for anchovies. Anchovies are food for other sea creatures. If there were no phytoplankton, there would be no energy source for the copepods. If there were no copepods there might be no anchovies. Then what would happen to the sea creatures?

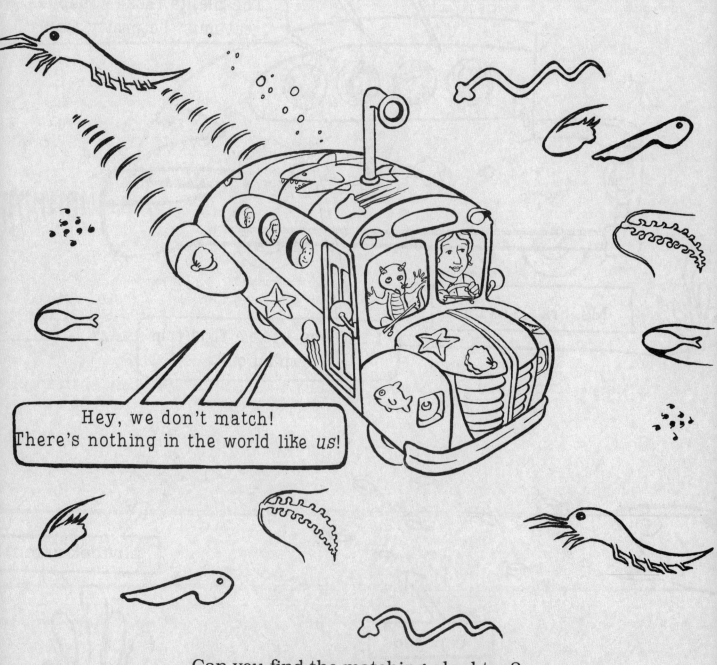

Hey, we don't match!
There's nothing in the world like *us*!

Can you find the matching plankton?
Answers on page 31.

Dinner Detective

Who eats whom? Read the clues. Then write the names in the blanks to make a food chain.

PHYTOPLANKTON
are plants. They don't eat animals.
They make their own food from sunlight.

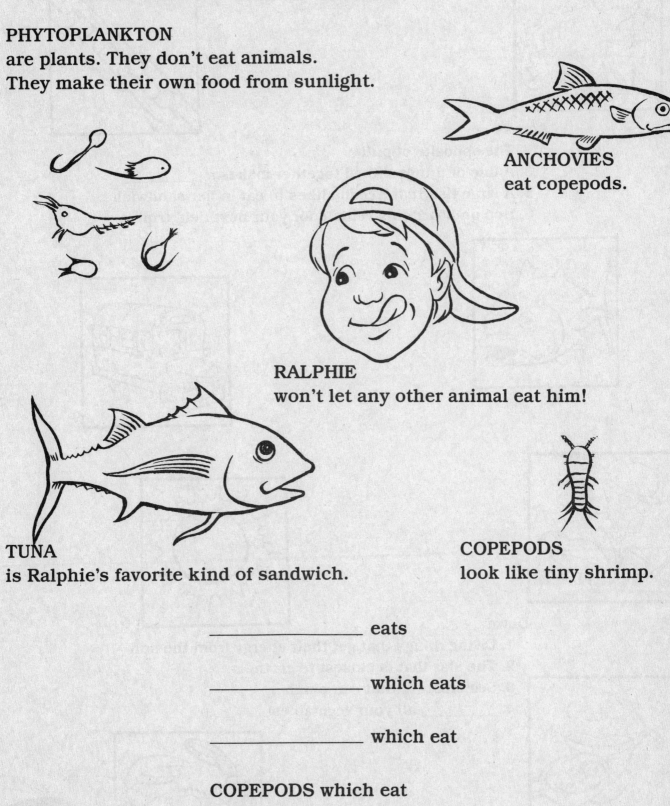

ANCHOVIES
eat copepods.

RALPHIE
won't let any other animal eat him!

TUNA
is Ralphie's favorite kind of sandwich.

COPEPODS
look like tiny shrimp.

_____ eats

_____ which eats

_____ which eat

COPEPODS which eat

_____ .

Answers on page 31.

Ocean Crossing

Use the clues to complete the puzzle on the next page.

Across

1. The opposite of *pull*
3. A line of things linked together makes a _____
5. A large fish that Keesha likes to eat in her sandwich
6. Hop on board this vehicle for your next field trip!

Down

1. Living things that get their energy from the sun
2. The star that is closest to earth
3. Sea creature that can pinch
4. _____ all your vegetables!

Answers on page 31.

Frizzle!

What's a seven-letter-word for one
who takes children on amazing trips?

Hard to Sea

Which of these things might you find hidden underwater?
Dive right in!

sea star

The Magic School Bus

ATLANTIS

scuba diver

oops — Ralphie's shoe

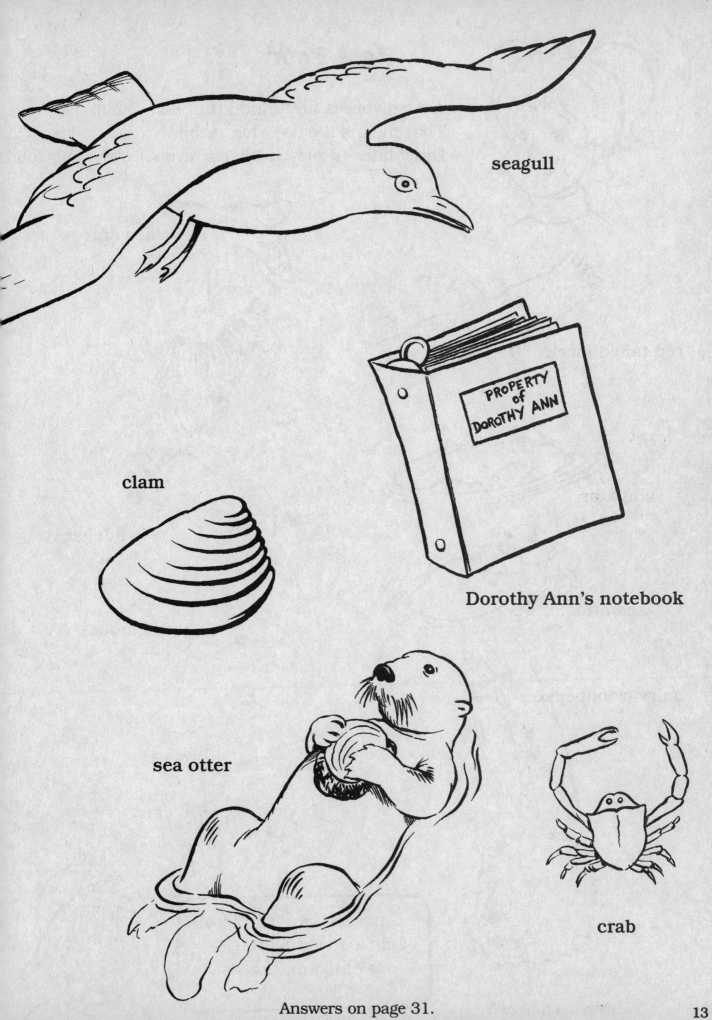

seagull

clam

PROPERTY of DOROTHY ANN

Dorothy Ann's notebook

sea otter

crab

Answers on page 31.

Fast Food

A carnivore is an animal that eats meat.
That means it eats other animals.
Draw lines to match the carnivores with their food.

sea star

zebra

wildebeest

mouse

duck

ants

red-tailed hawk

alligator

sea otter

hairy woodpecker

lion

Surprise! one of these
animals eats more than
one thing on the list.
Which is it?

Answers on page 31.

Scurry!

All animals that eat other animals are predators. *Predators*, such as hawks and foxes, hunt for their food. The animals they hunt are called *prey*. Some small animals protect themselves by moving quickly, hiding in holes or under rocks and plants, or by standing very still.

In the game of *Scurry!*, you are a small animal trying to hide from predators. Up to four people may play. The first player to reach home wins.

Here is what you'll need to play the game:

A different kind of coin for each player.
   A penny is a chipmunk.
   A nickel is a meadow vole.
   A dime is a mouse.
   A quarter is a rabbit.

One more coin (any kind) to toss.

The game board on the next two pages.

Now turn to page 18 to read how to play *Scurry!*

Scurry!

A game for 2 to 4 players.
See instructions on page 18.

Heads = 2 spaces
Tails = 1 space

START

You find delicious seeds.
Go ahead 3 spaces.

chipmunk

A hawk spots you.
Go back 2 spaces to hide.

mouse

red-tailed hawk

You take a shortcut through a
hollow log. Go ahead 3 spaces.

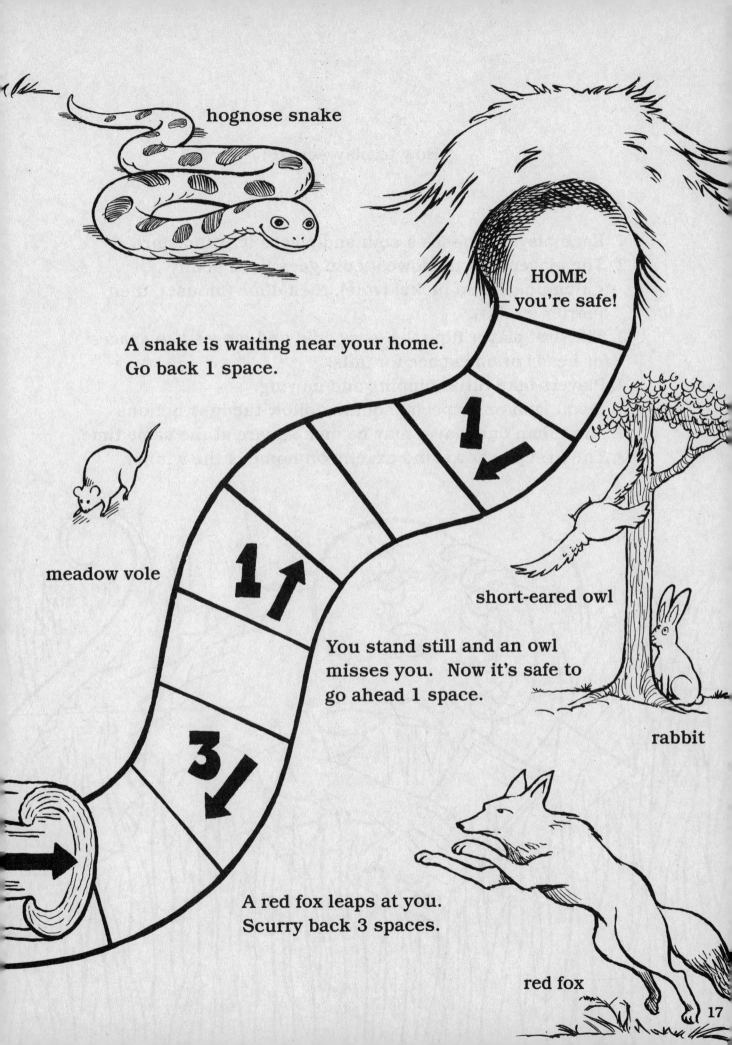

hognose snake

HOME
— you're safe!

A snake is waiting near your home.
Go back 1 space.

1 ↘

meadow vole

1 ↑

short-eared owl

You stand still and an owl
misses you. Now it's safe to
go ahead 1 space.

rabbit

3 ↘

A red fox leaps at you.
Scurry back 3 spaces.

red fox

How to play *Scurry!*

1. Each player chooses a coin and places it at the start.
2. The player with the lowest coin goes first: penny (chipmunk), then nickel (vole), then dime (mouse), then quarter (rabbit).
3. The first player flips the extra coin and moves two spaces for heads or one space for tails.
4. Players take turns flipping and moving.
5. If you land on a special square, follow the instructions.
6. More than one player may be on a square at the same time.
7. The first player to land exactly on home is the winner.

Camera Safari

Color this picture any way you'd like!

Queen of the Forest

Many animals in a food chain may eat some of the same things. That's why some people call a food chain a food web. The animal at the top of the web is not eaten by any other animal. Connect the dots to see the animal that is at the top of many food webs in northern forests.

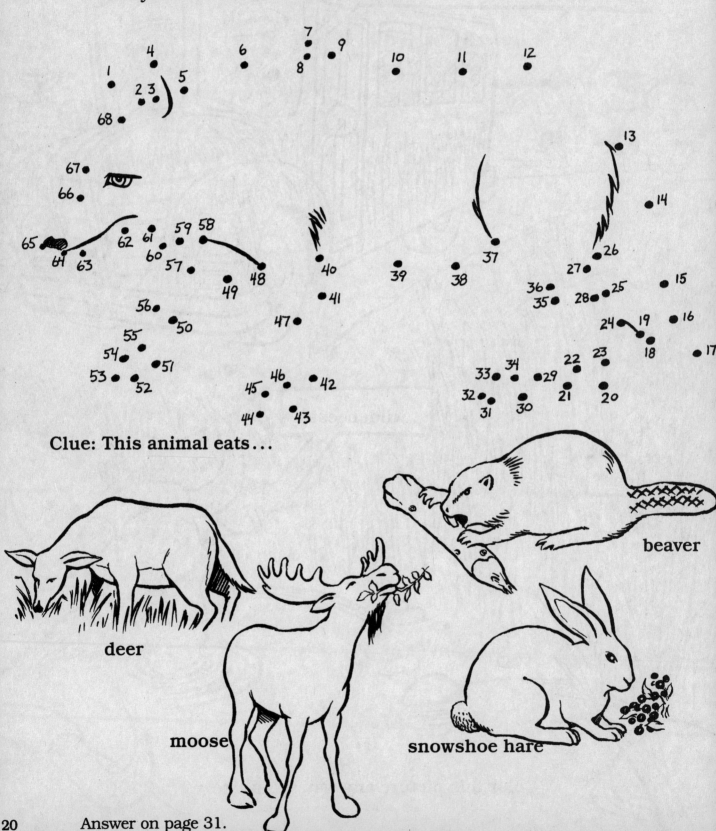

Clue: This animal eats...

deer

moose

beaver

snowshoe hare

Answer on page 31.

A Tangled Web

Uh-oh! Ms. Frizzle has gotten us into a really *sticky* situation this time. We are about to become a spider's lunch — just like the rest of these insects. Help us escape without touching the sticky threads of the web — or meeting up with the spider! Follow the maze.

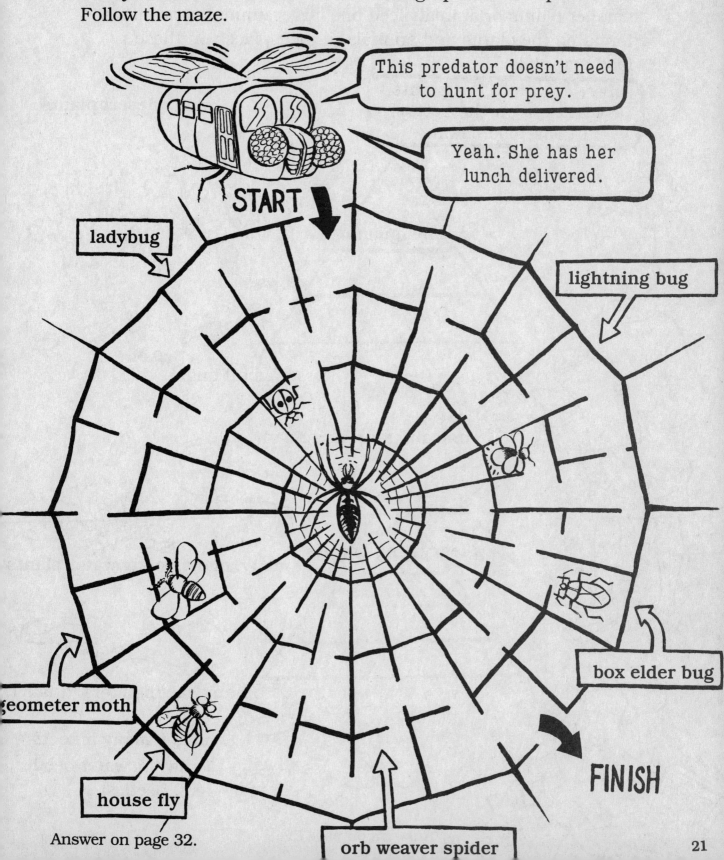

START

This predator doesn't need to hunt for prey.

Yeah. She has her lunch delivered.

ladybug

lightning bug

geometer moth

house fly

box elder bug

FINISH

orb weaver spider

Answer on page 32.

More or Less

It takes *lots* of smaller things at the bottom of a food chain to feed one larger animal at the top!

Drawing a food chain in a pyramid shape shows that many smaller plants or animals feed one larger animal. Draw lines to match the plants and animals to their places on these food pyramids.

Here's a hint: The plants are always on the bottom of the food chain.

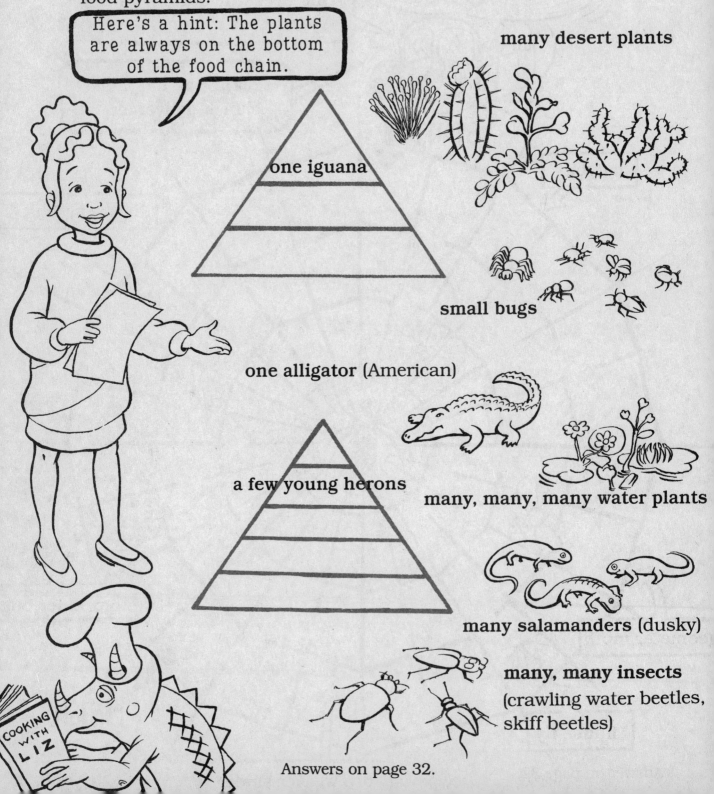

many desert plants

one iguana

small bugs

one alligator (American)

a few young herons

many, many, many water plants

many salamanders (dusky)

many, many insects
(crawling water beetles, skiff beetles)

Answers on page 32.

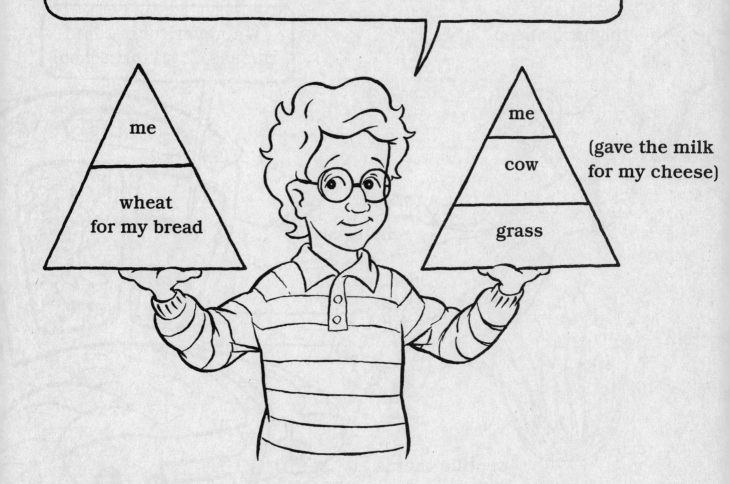

People are at the top of many food chains.
I had a cheese sandwich for lunch.
I drew these pyramids to show
the food chains in my lunch

me

wheat for my bread

me

cow

grass

(gave the milk for my cheese)

Fill in your own food chains! In each pyramid, draw yourself, draw something that you eat and, if your food comes from an animal, draw what it eats, too. Plants are at the bottom of every food chain.

me

what I eat

what it eats

Desert Dessert

Here's a California desert. It's a food chain in action! Color this picture any way you'd like.

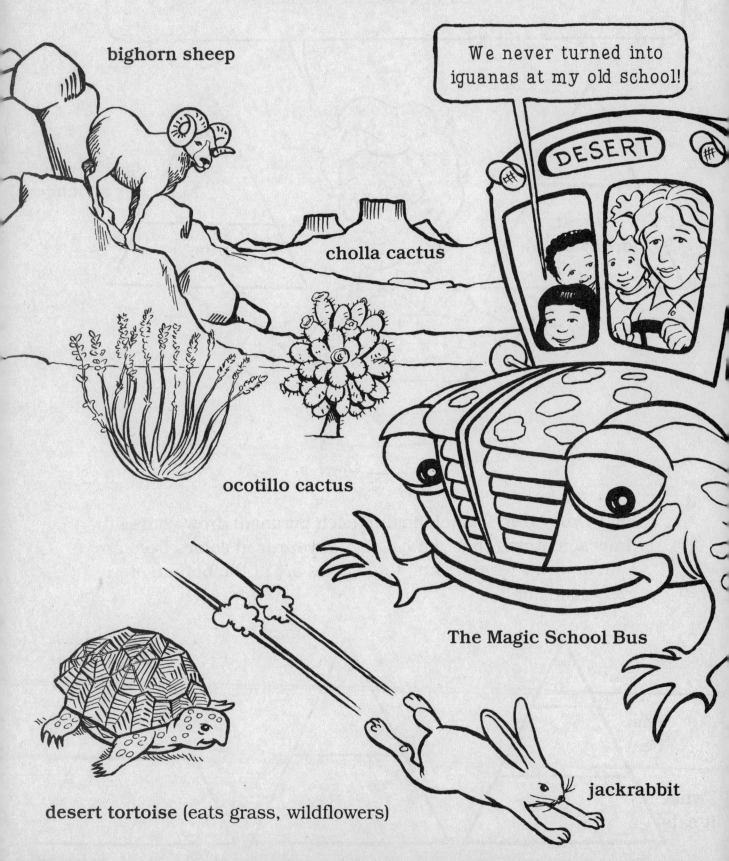

desert tortoise (eats grass, wildflowers)

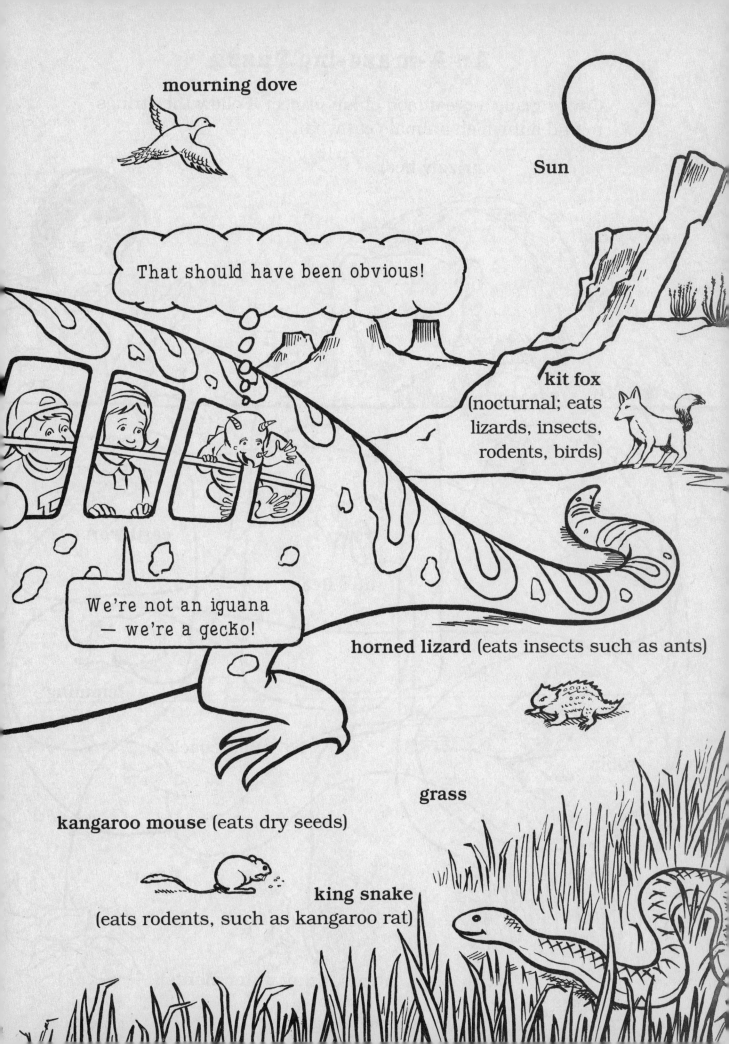

An A-maze-ing Puzzle

Carlos made a great food chain project. Follow the strings to find out which animals eat what.

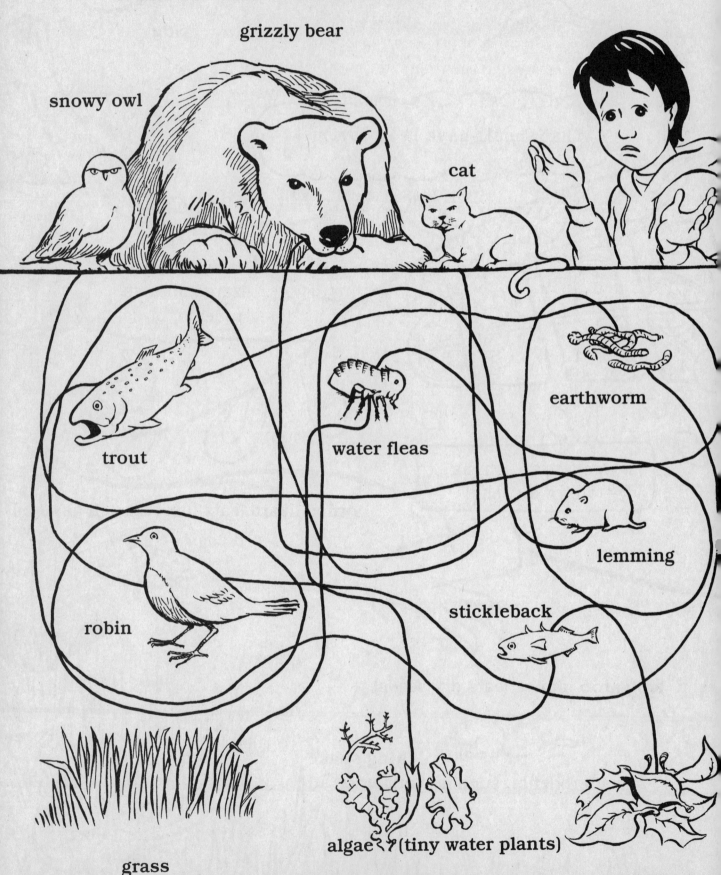

grizzly bear

snowy owl

cat

trout

water fleas

earthworm

lemming

robin

stickleback

algae (tiny water plants)

grass

leaves

Answers on page 32.

Chow Time

We're back at school — at last!
Our classroom pets are hungry.
Who gets what?
Draw lines to match the animals with their own foods.

rabbit

goldfish

anole

parrot

caterpillar

Answers on page 32.

It All Adds Up

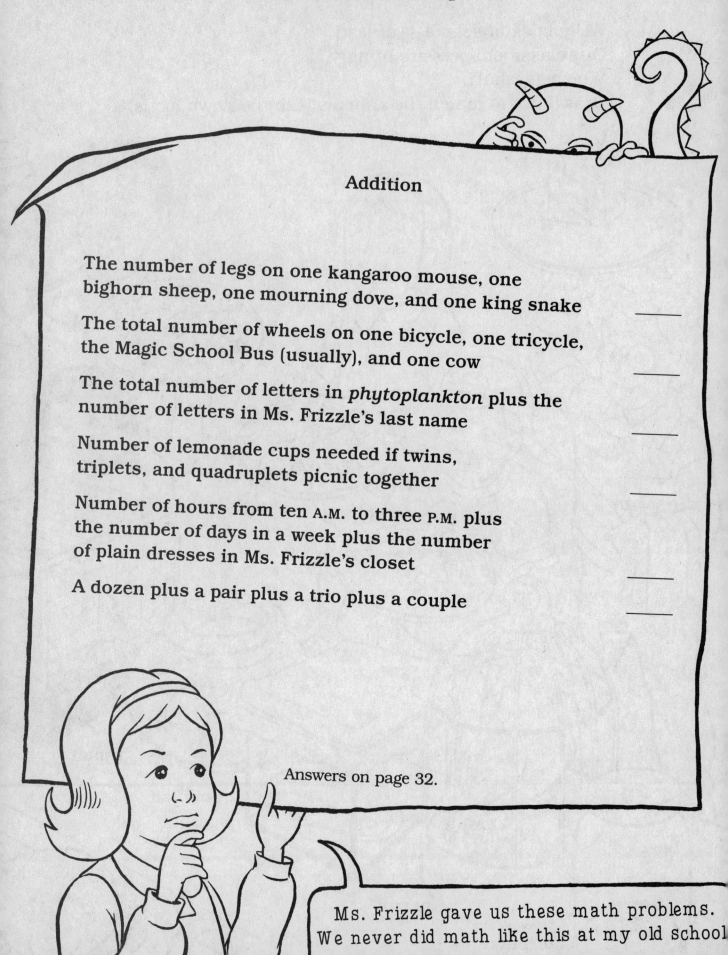

Addition

The number of legs on one kangaroo mouse, one bighorn sheep, one mourning dove, and one king snake _____

The total number of wheels on one bicycle, one tricycle, the Magic School Bus (usually), and one cow _____

The total number of letters in *phytoplankton* plus the number of letters in Ms. Frizzle's last name _____

Number of lemonade cups needed if twins, triplets, and quadruplets picnic together _____

Number of hours from ten A.M. to three P.M. plus the number of days in a week plus the number of plain dresses in Ms. Frizzle's closet _____

A dozen plus a pair plus a trio plus a couple _____

Answers on page 32.

Ms. Frizzle gave us these math problems. We never did math like this at my old school

Code à la Mode

A chain of food jokes!

Why can't a person starve in the desert?
Because of the sand which is there.

Get it? The *sandwiches there?*

What do giant pandas have that
no other animal has?
Baby pandas.

How do you catch a squirrel?
Climb up a tree and act like a nut.

The answers to these are in code.
Here's a hint: Write the first
letter of each word pictured.

APPLAUSE

What bird is at every meal?

_____   _____

What do you call a cow that eats grass?

_____   _____

Answers on page 32.

School, Sweet School!

What a day! Now we can munch on something in our own personal food chains. "Enjoy!" Ms. Frizzle says.

Color this picture any way you'd like!

Answers

page 4

TOMAT~O~

~HAY~

RI~CE~

GRA~SS~

LETT~UCE~

CORN

page 5

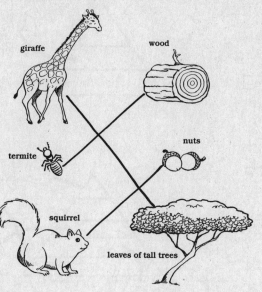

giraffe

wood

termite

nuts

squirrel

leaves of tall trees

page 8

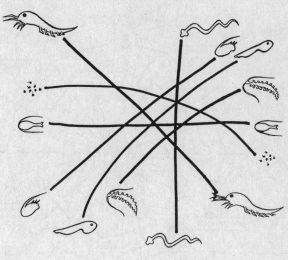

page 9

<u>RALPHIE</u> eats
<u>TUNA</u> which eats
<u>ANCHOVIES</u> which eat
<u>COPEPODS</u> which eat
<u>PHYTOPLANKTON.</u>

pages 10-11

	¹P	²S	H	
L	U			
³C	H	A	I	N
R		N		⁴E
A		⁵T	U	N	A
⁶B	U	S		T

pages 12-13

Scuba diver, crab,
sea star, clam,
the Magic School Bus.

page 14

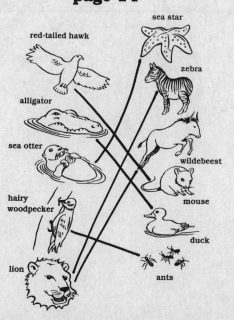

red-tailed hawk

sea star

zebra

alligator

sea otter

wildebeest

mouse

hairy
woodpecker

duck

lion

ants

The lion eats more than one thing.

page 20

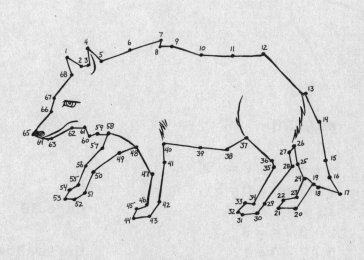

A gray wolf

page 21

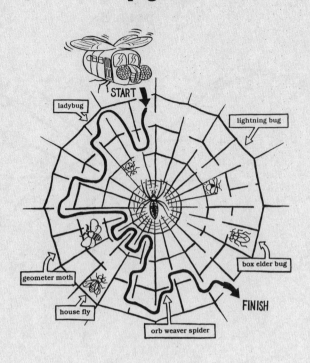

page 22

page 26

snowy owl
↓
lemming
↓
grass

grizzly bear
↓
trout
↓
stickleback
↓
water fleas
↓
algae
(tiny water plants)

cat
↓
robin
↓
earthworm
↓
leaves

page 27

page 28

4 + 4 + 2 + 0 = 10
2 + 3 + 4 + 0 = 9
13 + 7 = 20
2 + 3 + 4 = 9
5 + 7 + 0 = 12
12 + 2 + 3 + 2 = 19

page 29

the swallow

a lawn mooer